CGP has Year 1 Phonics sounded out!

CGP's Targeted Practice Books are packed with fun and friendly activities to build Year 1 pupils' confidence as they learn to read and write.

What's more, they follow the National Curriculum 'Letters and Sounds' programme, so you can be sure they cover everything children need to learn.

This is **Year 1 Targeted Practice Book 2**. It covers the second part of **Phase 5** of the 'Letters and Sounds' programme, including:

- Alternative pronunciations for:
  i, o, e, er, c, g, ow, ie, ea, u, ch, a, y, ou
- More **tricky words** and **silent letters**

What CGP is all about

Our sole aim here at CGP is to produce the highest quality books
— carefully written, immaculately presented and
dangerously close to being funny.

Then we work our socks off to get them out to you
— at the cheapest possible prices.

How to Use this Book

In this Book

You'll meet...

 Word Birds: they'll help you read and write words and sentences

 Chatty Bats: they'll tell your helper what words to say in writing activities

 Jolly Jugglers: they'll help you practise those tricky words

Hints for Helpers

Here are a few things to bear in mind when using this book:

- CGP's Phonics series aligns with **Letters and Sounds**, the Department for Education's systematic synthetic phonics programme. Reception books 1-5 cover Phases 1, 2, 3 and 4. The first Year 1 book centred on the early part of Phase 5. This book focuses on alternative pronunciations of letters for reading.

- The book should be worked through **in order**, as new content builds on content covered earlier in the book.

- '**Tricky words**' are words with letters that have a sound that does not correspond to the expected sound, or that have a sound that has not yet been learned. These words need to be practised until they can be read straight away without blending sounds.

- '**Word frames**' are used in spelling and writing activities. Word frames for words that can be sounded out have boxes. There is **one box for each sound**.

- The goal of all phonics programmes is to achieve **automatic recognition** of words without having to blend sounds. As a step towards that, **grey lines** under letters that work together to make one sound are **only shown in the introductions** on Reading Tricky Words pages. However, if any child needs the extra support, they can be encouraged to sound out words and draw their own lines.

- This resource requires children to match images to words. You may need to help children to **identify** some images they're not sure of.

Above all, promote a **positive, confident attitude** towards reading and writing by giving lots of praise and encouragement.

Contents

Written by Karen Bryant-Mole

Editors: Andy Cashmore, Christopher Lindle, Sam Mann, Sam Norman
Reviewers: Ross Knaggs, Stef Lake, Clare Leck
With thanks to Holly Robinson and Lucy Towle for the proofreading.
ISBN: 978 1 78908 017 9

Images throughout the book from www.edu-clips.com
Printed by Elanders Ltd, Newcastle upon Tyne.
Based on the classic CGP style created by Richard Parsons.

Year 1 Book 1 Check

Look at each card in turn. **Say** the sound.
Put a **tick** (✓) below each sound you can say.

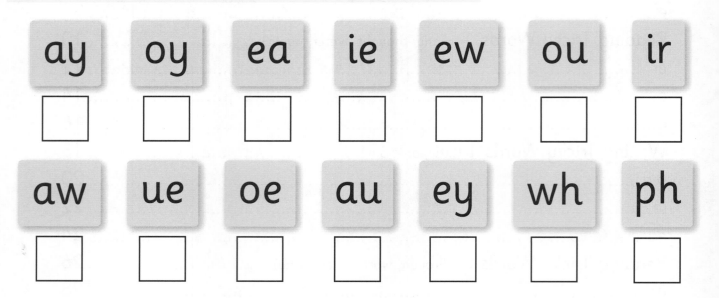

ay	oy	ea	ie	ew	ou	ir
☐	☐	☐	☐	☐	☐	☐

aw	ue	oe	au	ey	wh	ph
☐	☐	☐	☐	☐	☐	☐

Read the words under each picture. **Circle** the correct word.

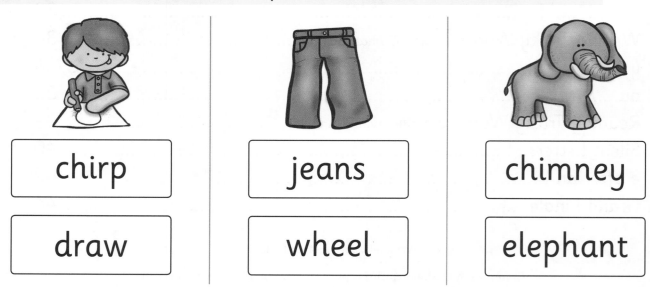

chirp	jeans	chimney
draw	wheel	elephant

Look at each block below.
If you can **read** the tricky word on the block, **circle** it.

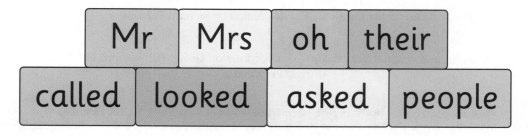

Mr   Mrs   oh   their

called   looked   asked   people

Phonics — Year 1 Book 2   © CGP — Not to be photocopied

Some letters work together but aren't written next to each other.
Read the words next to this picture. **Circle** the correct word.

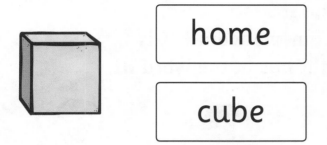

home

cube

Remember! In words like these, the letter for the last sound is tucked in between the letters that work together to make the middle sound.

Find the cards for the sound in the middle of **bike** and the sound in the middle of **cave**. **Complete** the words.

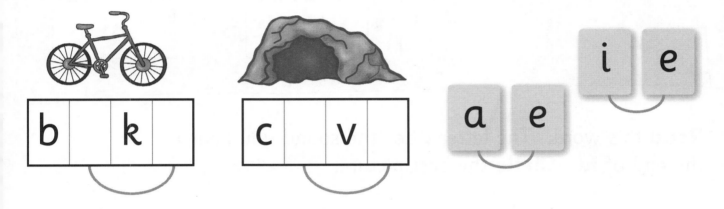

b		k

c		v

a   e

i   e

Listen to the tricky words these bats are saying.
Write each word in one of the special word frames.

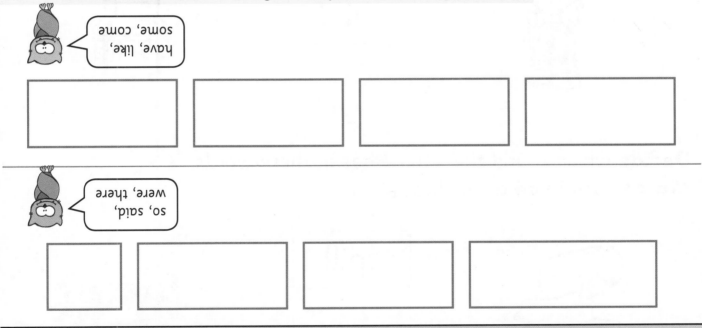

have, like, some, come

so, said, were, there

I can remember everything I learned in Book 1.

© CGP — Not to be photocopied

Phonics — Year 1 Book 2

i

i ← The sound this letter has in the word **hit** is different from the sound it has in the word **hi**.

Can you say the sound the letter has in **hit** and the sound it has in **hi**?

hit

hi

Read this word. The letter **i** has the sound you hear at the end of **hi**. **Circle** the best picture.

child

Decide which sound the letter **i** has in these words. **Match** each word to the best picture.

spill

spider

Read the sentences. **Match** each sentence to the correct picture.

An ant is a kind of insect.

Bluebells are wild flowers.

A pilot flies a plane.

Read the sentence. **Circle** the best picture for the sentence.

The driver spots a lion and a tiger.

I know that the letter 'i' can have the sound I hear at the end of 'hi'.

Phonics — Year 1 Book 2

o

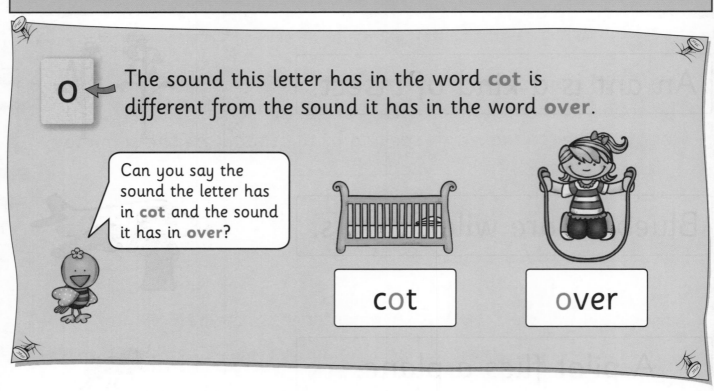

o ← The sound this letter has in the word **cot** is different from the sound it has in the word **over**.

Can you say the sound the letter has in **cot** and the sound it has in **over**?

cot

over

Read this word. The letter **o** has the sound you hear at the start of **over**. **Circle** the best picture.

post

Decide which sound each letter **o** has in these words. **Match** each word to the best picture.

photo

dolphin

Read the sentences. Match each sentence to the correct picture.

Hippos are good swimmers.

It is often cold in winter.

Most dogs have lots of fur.

Read the sentence. Circle the best picture for the sentence.

They both enjoy the open air.

I know that the letter 'o' can have
the sound I hear at the start of 'over'.

Phonics — Year 1 Book 2

e

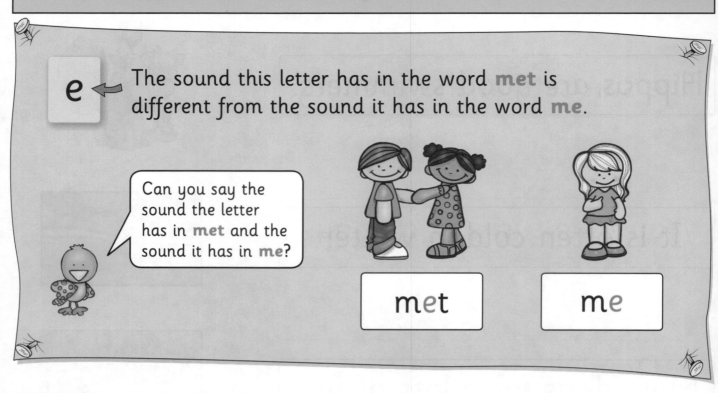

e ← The sound this letter has in the word **met** is different from the sound it has in the word **me**.

Can you say the sound the letter has in **met** and the sound it has in **me**?

met   me

Read this word. The letter **e** has the sound you hear at the end of **me**. **Circle** the best picture.

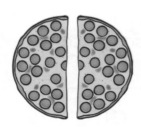

equal

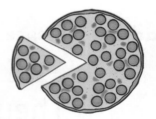

Decide which sound each letter **e** has in these words. **Match** each word to the best picture.

meteor

tent

Read the sentences. Match each sentence to the correct picture.

The sun sets in the evening.

You take turns in a relay.

Dandelions are weeds.

Read the sentence. Circle the best picture for the sentence.

The spell book held some evil secrets.

I know that the letter 'e' can have the sound I hear at the end of 'me'.

Reading Tricky Words 1

Let's learn some new tricky words.
These tricky words are **many**, **thought**, **water** and **again**.

| many | thought | water | again |

Some of the letters in tricky words have sounds you don't expect or haven't learned yet. Practise these words until you can read them straight away.

Read each caption. **Match** it to the correct picture.

many seeds

many petals

Look at the picture. **Read** the sentences.
Circle the best sentence for the picture.

She thought it looked cute.

She thought it looked mean.

Phonics — Year 1 Book 2

Read each question. Circle the best answer.

What do all living things need?

sweets   water

When will you go to bed again?

tonight   next week

Read the sentences. Circle the best picture for the sentences.

The children thought the water park was fun. There were many rides. They went on them again and again!

I can read the tricky words 'many', 'thought', 'water' and 'again'.

Phonics — Year 1 Book 2

er

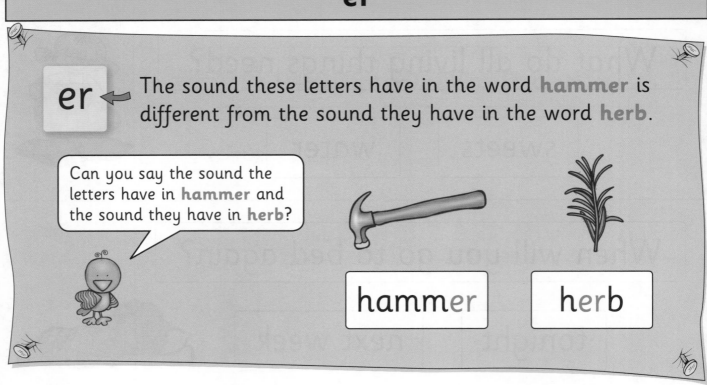

er The sound these letters have in the word **hammer** is different from the sound they have in the word **herb**.

Can you say the sound the letters have in **hammer** and the sound they have in **herb**?

hammer   herb

Read this word. The letters **e** and **r** work together. They have the sound you hear in the middle of **herb**. **Circle** the best picture.

perfume

The **u** and the **e** are working together. The letter for the last sound is tucked in between them.

Decide which sound the letters **e** and **r** have when they work together in these words. **Match** each word to the best picture.

mermaid

drummer

Phonics — Year 1 Book 2

Read the sentences. **Match** each sentence to the correct picture.

A tern is a sort of seabird.

Stern means the same as strict.

Moles are experts at digging.

Read the sentence. **Circle** the best picture for the sentence.

Fern herds her sheep.

I know that the letters 'e' and 'r' can have
the sound I hear in the middle of 'herb'.

Phonics — Year 1 Book 2

c

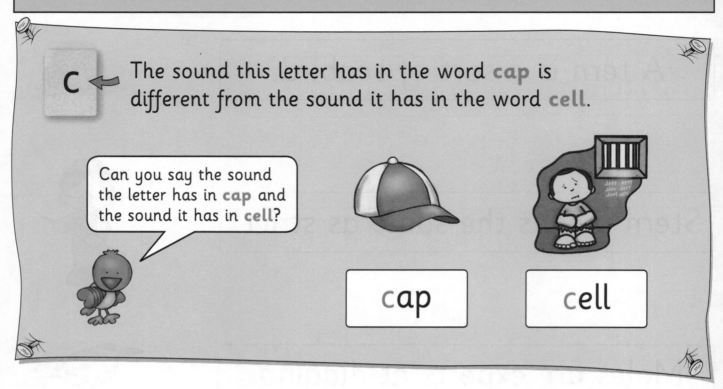

c ← The sound this letter has in the word **cap** is different from the sound it has in the word **cell**.

Can you say the sound the letter has in **cap** and the sound it has in **cell**?

cap

cell

Read this word. The letter **c** has the sound you hear at the start of **cell**. **Circle** the best picture.

The **i** and the **e** are working together here.

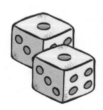

mice

Decide which sound each letter **c** has in these words. **Match** each word to the best picture.

princess

crocodile

Read the sentences. **Match** each sentence to the correct picture.

| Pencils need sharp points. |

| You see clowns in a circus. |

| Rockets travel into space. |

Read the sentence. **Circle** the best picture for the sentence.

| It's nice to win first place in a race. |

I know that the letter 'c' can have
the sound I hear at the start of 'cell'.

Phonics — Year 1 Book 2

g

g ← The sound this letter has in the word **goat** is different from the sound it has in the word **gem**.

Can you say the sound the letter has in **goat** and the sound it has in **gem**?

goat

gem

Read this word. The letter **g** has the sound you hear at the start of **gem**. **Circle** the best picture.

The **a** and the **e** are working together here.

cage

Decide which sound the letter **g** has in these words. **Match** each word to the best picture.

girls

gerbil

Read the sentences. Match each sentence to the correct picture.

Germs can make you sick.

Magic can amaze you.

Actors perform on stage.

Read the sentence. Circle the best picture for the sentence.

The huge giant was in a rage.

I know that the letter 'g' can have
the sound I hear at the start of 'gem'.

Phonics — Year 1 Book 2

Writing Tricky Words 1

Let's spell some of the tricky words you can already read.
Learn which letters are needed to write each word.

Tricky words have special word frames.
There isn't a separate box for each sound.
You just write the whole word in the frame.

Name the letters in the words **little**, **one** and **out**.
Copy the letters into the special word frames.

little	one	out

Listen carefully to the sentence the bat is saying.
Write the sentence in the word frames.

Pam has gifts.

Spell the name just as it sounds.

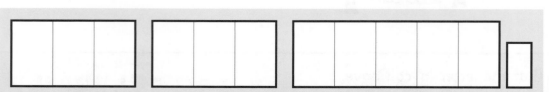

Here are three more bats. **Listen** to the sentence each bat is saying, then **write** it in the word frames.

I can write sentences that include the tricky words 'little', 'one' and 'out'.

Phonics — Year 1 Book 2

ow

ow ← The sound these letters have in the word **owl** is different from the sound they have in the word **mow**.

Can you say the sound the letters have in **owl** and the sound they have in **mow**?

owl

mow

Read this word. The letters **o** and **w** work together. They have the sound you hear at the end of **mow**. **Circle** the best picture.

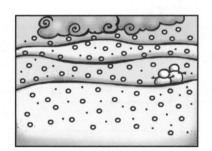

snow

Decide which sound the letters **o** and **w** have when they work together in these words. **Match** each word to the best picture.

rainbow

tower

Read the sentences. Match each sentence to the correct picture.

Bowls are often made of clay.

Pillows feel soft to lie on.

Some animals glow at night.

Read the sentence. Circle the best picture for the sentence.

She shows off her yellow bows.

I know that the letters 'o' and 'w' can have
the sound I hear at the end of 'mow'.

ie

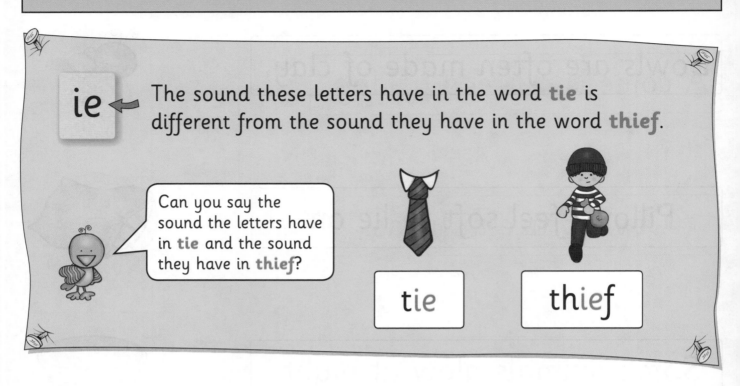

ie → The sound these letters have in the word **tie** is different from the sound they have in the word **thief**.

Can you say the sound the letters have in **tie** and the sound they have in **thief**?

tie

thief

Read this word. The letters **i** and **e** work together. They have the sound you hear in the middle of **thief**. **Circle** the best picture.

shield

Decide which sound the letters **i** and **e** have when they work together in these words. **Match** each word to the best picture.

priest

pies

Read the sentences. Match each sentence to the correct picture.

A collie is a breed of dog.

Cows graze in fields.

A shriek is a high scream.

Read the sentence. Circle the best picture for the sentence.

Ollie and Ellie make brownies and cookies.

I know that the letters 'i' and 'e' can have
the sound I hear in the middle of 'thief'.

Phonics — Year 1 Book 2

ea

ea ← The sound these letters have in the word **heap** is different from the sound they have in the word **head**.

Can you say the sound the letters have in **heap** and the sound they have in **head**?

heap

head

Read this word. The letters **e** and **a** work together. They have the sound you hear in the middle of **head**. **Circle** the best picture.

breath

Decide which sound the letters **e** and **a** have when they work together in these words. **Match** each word to the best picture.

weather

teapot

Read the sentences. **Match** each sentence to the correct picture.

All birds have feathers.

Running can make you sweat.

A web is made of threads.

Read the sentence. **Circle** the best picture for the sentence.

I spread jam on my bread at breakfast.

I know that the letters 'e' and 'a' can have
the sound I hear in the middle of 'head'.

Phonics — Year 1 Book 2

Reading Tricky Words 2

Let's learn some more tricky words.
These tricky words are through, work, where and who.

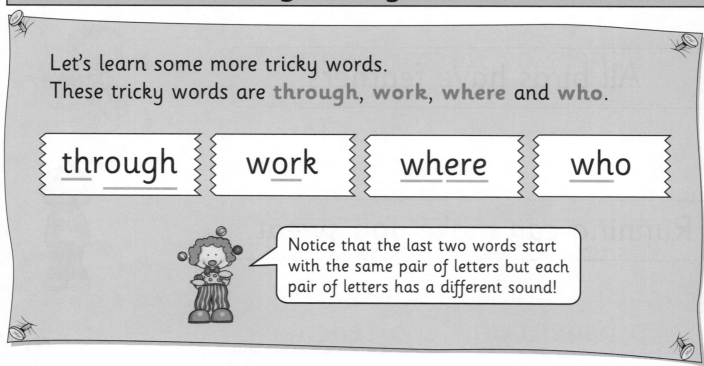

through   work   where   who

Notice that the last two words start with the same pair of letters but each pair of letters has a different sound!

Read each caption. **Match** it to the best picture.

through the tunnel

through the woods

Look at the picture. **Read** the questions.
Circle the best question for the picture.

Who and where are useful words to know. You often see them at the start of questions.

Who are you?

Where are you?

27

Read each question. **Circle** the correct answer.

Where do doctors work?

in a hospital   on a farm

Who works with children?

a fisherman   a teacher

Read the sentences. **Circle** the best picture for the sentences.

There had been a crime. Tom worked through the night. He found out who did it and where they went.

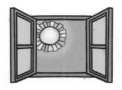

I can read the tricky words 'through', 'work', 'where' and 'who'.

Phonics — Year 1 Book 2

u

u ← The sound this letter has in the word **hut** is different from the sound it has in the word **uniform**.

Can you say the sound the letter has in **hut** and the sound it has in **uniform**?

hut

uniform

Decide which sound the letter **u** has in these words.
Match each word to the best picture.

duck

human

Say the word **bush**. What sound did you say for the letter **u**? **Colour** the picture.

bush

Some people say **bush** and **hut** with the same sound in the middle. Other people say these words with different sounds in the middle.

Read the sentences. Match each sentence to the correct picture.

Unicorns are not real.

Cats are popular pets.

You have to push a trolley.

Read the sentence. Circle the best picture for the sentence.

The music tutor conducts the pupils.

I know that the letter 'u' can have
the sound I hear at the start of 'uniform'.

Phonics — Year 1 Book 2

ch

ch ← The sounds these letters have in the names **Chelsea**, **Chris** and **Charlene** are all different.

Can you say the three different sounds?

Chelsea   Chris   Charlene

Decide which sound the letters **c** and **h** have when they work together in these words. **Match** each word to the best picture.

| march | chef | ache |

 The **a** and the **e** are working together here.

Read the sentences. Match each sentence to the correct picture.

Mechanics can fix things.

You find an anchor on a ship.

A parachute fills with air.

Read the sentence. Circle the best picture for the sentence.

The school orchestra plays a tune.

I know that the letters 'c' and 'h' can have the sounds
I hear at the start of 'Chris' and 'Charlene'.

Phonics — Year 1 Book 2

a

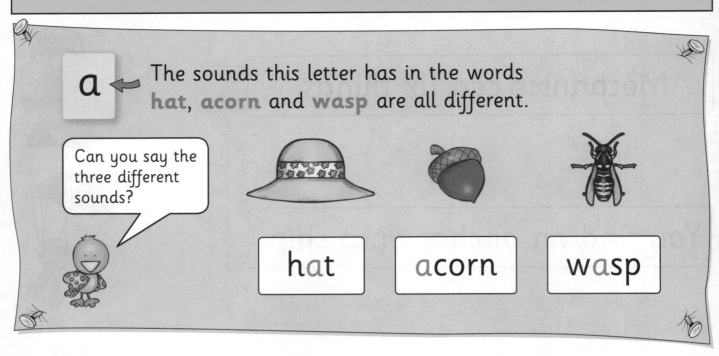

a ← The sounds this letter has in the words **hat**, **acorn** and **wasp** are all different.

Can you say the three different sounds?

| hat | acorn | wasp |

Decide which sound the letter **a** has in these words. **Match** each word to the best picture.

| map | swan | potato |

Say the word **grass**. What sound did you say for the letter **a**? **Colour** the picture.

grass

Some people say **grass** and **hat** with the same sound in the middle. Other people say these words with different sounds in the middle.

Read the sentences. Match each sentence to the correct picture.

A graph is a sort of chart.

Bacon goes well with eggs.

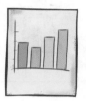

You can wash in a basin.

Read the sentence. Circle the best picture for the sentence.

Seth drank a glass of apricot squash.

I know some of the sounds that the letter 'a' can have.

Phonics — Year 1 Book 2

Writing Tricky Words 2

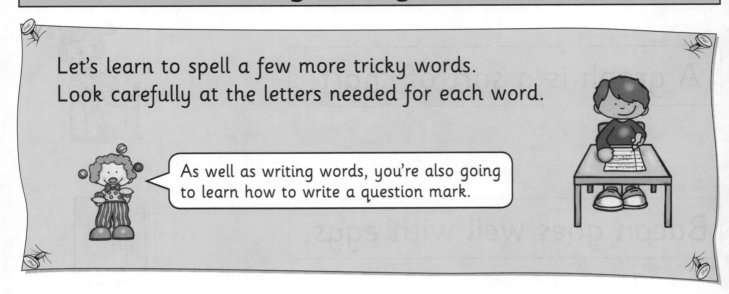

Let's learn to spell a few more tricky words.
Look carefully at the letters needed for each word.

As well as writing words, you're also going to learn how to write a question mark.

Name the letters in the words **when**, **what** and **do**.
Copy the letters into the special word frames.

when	what	do

You often see these words at the start of questions.

Questions always end with a **question mark**.
Look at the grey question mark. **Trace** over it with your finger.
Copy each black question mark into the box below.

Start at the red dot.
Go around and down.
Then add a dot.

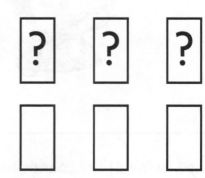

Listen to the question each bat is saying, then **write** it in the word frames. Don't forget the question mark at the end.

I can write sentences that include the tricky words 'when', 'what' and 'do'.

Phonics — Year 1 Book 2

y

The sounds this letter has in the words **yap**, **lolly**, **cry** and **gym** are all different.

Can you say the four different sounds?

| yap | lolly | cry | gym |

Decide which sound the letter **y** has in these words.
Match each word to the best picture.

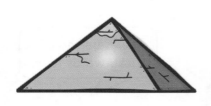

 pyramid

yell

empty

shy

Read the sentences. Match each sentence to the correct picture.

Stars shine in the night sky.

Chewing gum is sticky.

The symbol for plus is a cross.

Read the sentence. Circle the best picture for the sentence.

I am very happy with my wobbly jelly.

I know some of the sounds that the letter 'y' can have.

Phonics — Year 1 Book 2

ou

ou ← The sounds these letters have in the words **shout**, **mould** and **youth** are all different.

Can you say the three different sounds?

shout   mould   youth

Decide which sound the letters **o** and **u** have when they work together in these words. **Match** each word to the best picture.

shoulder   soup   mouth

I know some of the sounds that the letters 'o' and 'u' can have.

Reading Tricky Words 3

These tricky words are **could**, **would** and **should**.
The sound in the middle of each word is the same. The letters that work together to make this spelling of the sound are the same too.

c<u>ou</u>ld   w<u>ou</u>ld   sh<u>ou</u>ld

Read the sentences. **Match** each sentence to the best picture.

Some of these words have sounds you practised on the opposite page.

I would like to help you out.

He could not lift the boulder.

She should join a pop group.

I can read the tricky words 'could', 'would' and 'should'.

Phonics — Year 1 Book 2

Silent Letters

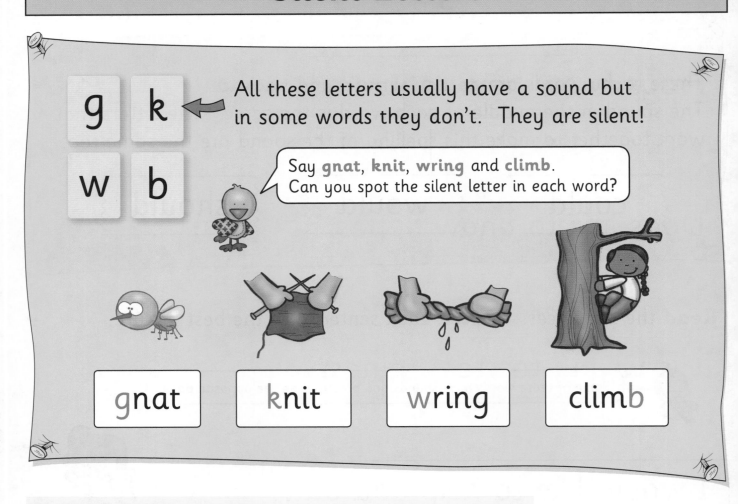

g k

w b

All these letters usually have a sound but in some words they don't. They are silent!

Say **gnat**, **knit**, **wring** and **climb**. Can you spot the silent letter in each word?

gnat   knit   wring   climb

Read these words. Each word has a silent letter.
Match each word to its picture.

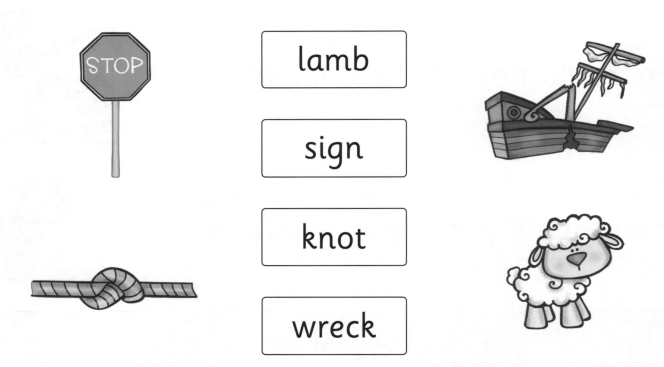

lamb

sign

knot

wreck

Read the sentences. Match each sentence to the correct picture.

Frogs know how to jump.

Dogs like to gnaw bones.

It is wrong to steal things.

Read the sentence. Circle the best picture for the sentence.

Sam hurt his knee, his wrist and his thumb.

I know that some letters in certain words have no sound at all.

e after an l

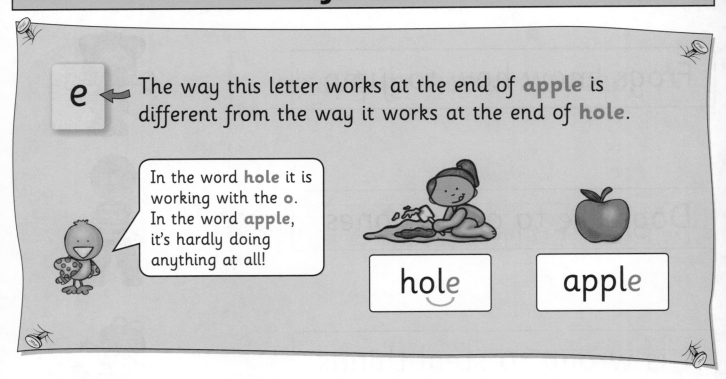

e ← The way this letter works at the end of **apple** is different from the way it works at the end of **hole**.

In the word **hole** it is working with the **o**. In the word **apple**, it's hardly doing anything at all!

hole

apple

Read this word. **Circle** the best picture.

needle

Read these words. **Match** each word to its picture.

capsule

candle

One **e** is working hard. The other is being a bit lazy.

Read the sentences. **Match** each sentence to the correct picture.

A jigsaw is a sort of puzzle.

You can boil water in a kettle.

A turtle has a hard shell.

Read the sentence. **Circle** the best picture for the sentence.

The tickle made the little baby giggle.

I know that when the letters 'l' and 'e' are together at the end of words, the 'e' can work in different ways.

Grand Finale

Read each word.
Find them hidden among the letters on the snake. Circle them.

slow	chief	rice	salt

These pictures show the life cycle of a butterfly.
Read the captions, then match them to the correct picture.

butterfly

caterpillar

chrysalis

egg

Do you like fairy tales?
Match the name of each story to the picture of the main character.

Little Red Riding Hood

The Gingerbread Man

Words in book titles usually start with a capital letter.

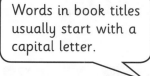

Cinderella

There is a fairy tale called Snow White and the Seven Dwarfs.
Read the names. **Match** each dwarf to his name.

Sneezy

Doc

Grumpy

Happy

Sleepy

Bashful

Dopey

Did you know that **bashful** means **shy**?

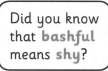

Some words have the same spelling but their sounds and meanings are different. **Match** each of these sentences to the correct picture.

The wind is blowing hard.

Yo-yos wind down and up.

The flowers are in a row.

Nell and Ted had a row.

Let's finish with a joke!
Read the question. Can you **guess** the answer?
Turn the workbook upside down. **Read** the answer.

Why did the maths book look sad?

¡smǝlqoɹd ɟo ʇol ɐ pɐɥ ʇI

I've had fun practising what I've learned.